Rhyme Time

Rhyming words have the same ending sound.

Say the name of each picture. Circle the two pictures that rhyme in each row.

Check the Signs

Say the name of each picture. Circle the animal with the picture that rhymes with the first picture in each row.

Scholastic Success With

BRAIN PLAY™

Preschool-1st Grade
2ND EDITION

Workbook

NEW YORK • TORONTO • LONDON • AUCKLAND • SYDNEY
MEXICO CITY • NEW DELHI • HONG KONG • BUENOS AIRES

Acknowledgments

From *Get Ready for Kindergarten.* Published by Scholastic Teaching Resources/Scholastic Inc. Copyright © 2004 by Scholastic Inc. Reprinted with permission.

From *Get Ready for 1st Grade.* Published by Scholastic Teaching Resources/Scholastic Inc. Copyright © 2004 by Scholastic Inc. Reprinted with permission.

Interior illustrations by Janet Armbrust, Abby Carter, Maxie Chambliss, Sue Dennen, Shelly Dietrich, Jane Dippold, Rusty Fletcher, James Graham Hale, Sherry Neidigh, Cary Pillo, and Carol Tiernon

ISBN 0-439-92830-3

17 16 15 14   23   11 10 9 8

Table of Contents

GRAMMAR

LOGIC

PHONICS

Time for Rhymes

Rhyming words have the same ending sound.

Say the name of each picture. Circle the two pictures that rhyme in each group.

Show What You Know

Say the name of each picture. Fill in the circle next to the word that rhymes.

1. ○ big ○ cat ○ bet	2. ○ set ○ bat ○ new	3. ○ rip ○ lap ○ can
4. ○ jet ○ jump ○ hug	5. ○ sink ○ wet ○ wing	6. ○ flag ○ vest ○ fan
7. ○ best ○ well ○ bit	8. ○ dish ○ fit ○ fizz	9. ○ rip ○ king ○ rest

Food Puzzles

Say the name of each food. Find the letter that stands for the beginning sound of each food. Draw a line from each food to its beginning letter sound.

1.

 s

2.

 m

3.

 t

4.

 p

5.

 b

Whose Toy Is It?

Read the names on the children's T-shirts aloud. Each child plays only with toys whose names begin with the same sound as his or her name. Fill in the letter that each toy begins with. Then draw lines from each child to the matching toys.

_____ adio   _____ ebra   _____ oll

Dan   Rosa   Zeb

_____ uck   _____ oo   _____ obot

Face First

The pictures show animal faces. Can you name each animal?
Write the letter that each animal's name begins with.

1. _____

2. _____

3. _____

4. _____

5. _____

6. _____

7. _____

8. _____

Hidden Letters

Say the name of each picture aloud. Look for the hidden letters that stand for the beginning sound of that name. Circle the hidden letters and then write the letters on the lines.

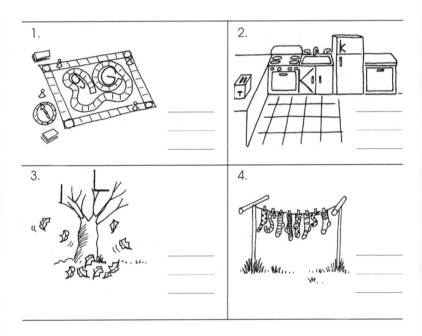

Show What You Know

Say the name of each picture. Fill in the circle next to the letter that
stands for the missing sound. Write the letter on the line.

1. ○ d ○ b ○ y _____ _____ uck	2. ○ q ○ x ○ p _____ _____ ueen	3. ○ v ○ w ○ t _____ _____ est
4. ○ b ○ p ○ h _____ _____ at	5. ○ g ○ c ○ j _____ _____ at	6. ○ p ○ f ○ d _____ _____ ish
7. ○ l ○ k ○ h _____ _____ ite	8. ○ x ○ z ○ y _____ _____ ebra	9. ○ r ○ n ○ m _____ _____ ope
10. ○ t ○ l ○ h _____ _____ ape	11. ○ g ○ r ○ s _____ _____ oat	12. ○ r ○ b ○ j _____ _____ ike

What's New?

Each bear has something new.

To find out what it is, say the name of each picture next to the bear.
Listen for the beginning sound.

Write the letter that stands for that sound under the picture.

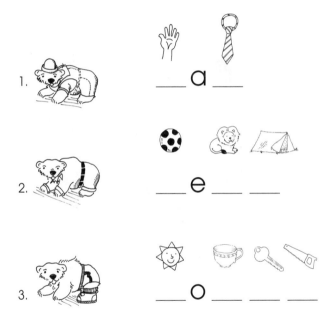

1. ___ a ___

2. ___ e ___ ___

3. ___ o ___ ___ ___

Get Tug's Mail

Tug the Bug wants to get his mail. Help him climb down the steps. Fill in the blank spaces with vowels to complete the words.

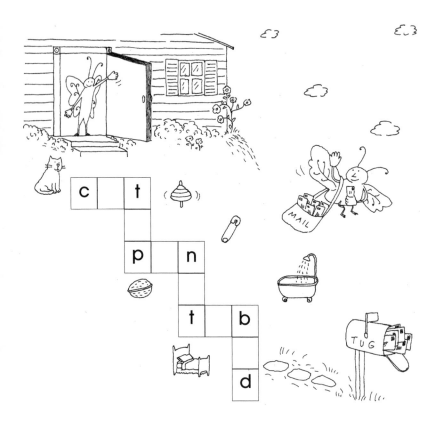

Short Vowel Crosswords

Use the picture clues to add a short vowel to each puzzle.

1.
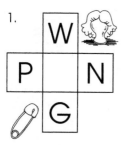

2.

3.
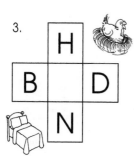

4.

5.

-at Family

Put the letters together to make the -at sound.

1. c + at = _____

2. b + at = _____

3. r + at = _____

4. h + at = _____

Look at the letters at the bottom of the page. Write them in the correct squares to finish each sentence.

5. Humpty Dumpty ☐ at on a wall.

6. It was as ☐ at as a pancake.

7. I like to ☐ at on the telephone.

8. He coughed and ☐ at out a gnat.

| fl | s | sp | ch |

-in Family

Put the letters together to make the *-in* sound.

1. ch + in = _____

2. tw + in = _____

3. p + in = _____

4. f + in = _____

Look at the letters at the bottom of the page. Write them in the correct squares to finish each sentence.

5. Sam wants to ☐ in the race.

6. Let's ☐ in the top again.

7. The ball hit me on the ☐ in.

8. A ☐ in is a kind of smile.

| gr | sh | sp | w |

-ug Family

Put the letters together to make the *-ug* sound.

1. h + ug = _____

2. m + ug = _____

3. j + ug = _____

4. b + ug = _____

Look at the letters at the bottom of the page. Write them in the correct squares to finish each sentence.

5. I ☐ug in the sand with a shovel.

6. Blankets keep us warm and ☐ug.

7. He gave the string a ☐ug.

8. Let's ☐ug the hole.

pl	d	sn	t

-op Family

Put the letters together to make the -op sound.

1. t + op = _____

2. st + op = _____

3. m + op = _____

4. c + op = _____

Look at the letters at the bottom of the page. Write them in the correct squares to finish each sentence.

5. He can ☐ op wood with an axe.

6. Let's ☐ op like rabbits.

7. The farmer had a ☐ op of corn.

8. We ☐ op at the mall.

| cr | sh | h | ch |

-est Family

Put the letters together to make the *-est* sound.

1. v + est = _____

2. n + est = _____

3. ch + est = _____

4. p + est = _____

Look at the letters at the bottom of the page. Write them in the correct squares to finish each sentence.

5. He is tired. He needs to ☐est.

6. Do your ☐est work.

7. Travel east, not ☐est.

8. I'm ready to take the ☐est.

| b | r | w | t |

-ock Family

Put the letters together to make the *-ock* sound.

1. r + ock = _____

2. s + ock = _____

3. cl + ock = _____

4. d + ock = _____

Look at the letters at the bottom of the page. Write them in the correct squares to finish each sentence.

5. Put on a ☐ ock before you paint.

6. A ☐ ock of geese flew south.

7. Did you hear a ☐ ock at the door?

8. We need to ☐ ock the gate.

l	kn	fl	sm

Word Search

How many words can you find? Look for the words below and circle them.

a	n	b	e	b	i	g	f	o	r
n	a	l	o	i	s	v	u	n	m
d	p	u	g	g	o	t	n	m	a
w	q	e	b	c	n	h	l	k	k
e	r	d	c	h	e	r	j	s	e
c	f	e	i	i	h	e	i	e	u
r	u	n	t	u	p	e	s	e	t
d	o	w	n	a	m	a	k	o	n
l	w	e	r	t	o	p	m	y	t
y	o	u	m	p	l	a	y	a	m

am	at	blue	go	make	one	see	we
an	be	down	is	my	play	three	you
and	big	for	it	on	run	to	

MATH

Mrs. Tacky Turtle

Circle the number that tells how many Mrs. Turtle is wearing.

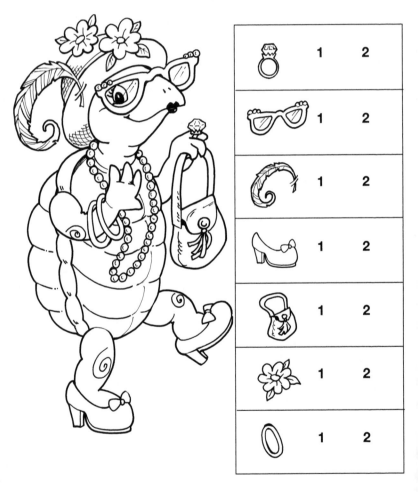

Climb to the Top

Count the objects on each step.
Circle the matching number.

Two Make a Pair

Count the shapes on each shoe. Draw a line to the matching number.

4

5

6

5

4

6

Seashells by the Seashore

Circle the number that tells how many.

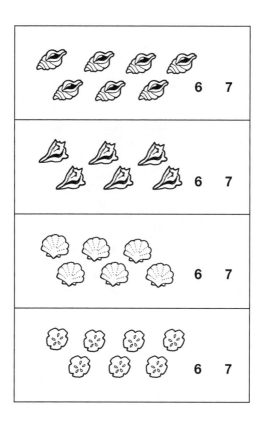

Going to the Market

Count the fruits. Write how many.

Number Practice: 10

Number Hunt

Circle every number 10.

2   4   26   40   3 | 8   10   9   25

10   25   3   9   8 | 2   21   5   7

3   0   5   4   3   10   0   5   8   10

7   10   8   10   14   9   3   0   29 |

Catch the Ball!

Count. Write how many.

Crawl Before You Fly

Connect the dots from **1** to **10**.

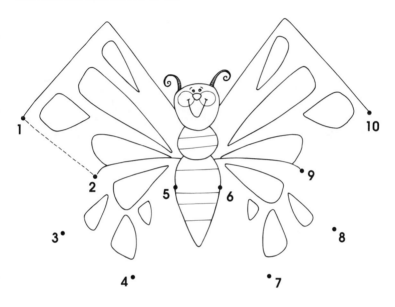

Shape Match-Up

Trace each shape. Draw a line to match each object to its shape.
Color the shapes.

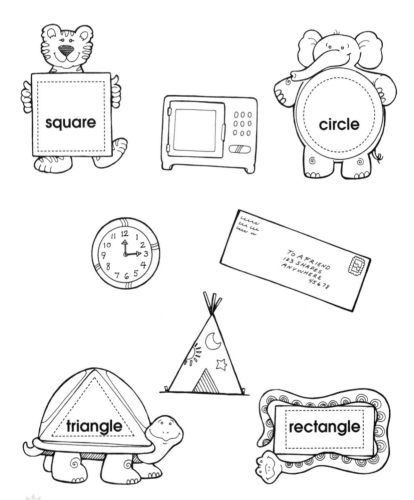

square

circle

triangle

rectangle

Shape Teasers

Color each shape using the code.

◯ = red   △ = blue   ▭ = green   ▢ = yellow

Naming Shapes

1. Draw a line matching each shape to its name.

triangle

circle

square

rectangle

2. Make an X on the shape that does not belong in the row.

3. Which shape looks like a balloon?

4. Which shape has four corners?

5. Which shape looks like an egg?

Tricks for Treats

Count the bones each dog has. In each box, circle the dog
with **less** bones.

A Penny in Your Pocket

A penny equals 1¢. Count the pennies in each pocket.
Write the total.

1. _____ ¢

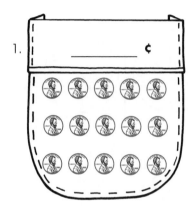

2. _____ ¢

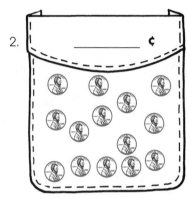

3. _____ ¢

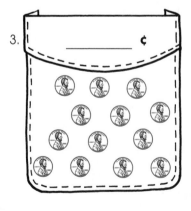

4. _____ ¢

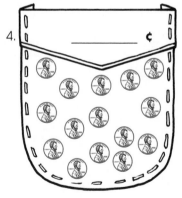

Telling Time

Write the time shown on each clock on the line.

1. ___ : ___

2. ___ : ___

3. ___ : ___

4. ___ : ___

5. ___ : ___

6. ___ : ___

7. ___ : ___

8. ___ : ___

Math

Time

Half Past or Thirty Minutes

The time 12:30 can be read as twelve thirty or half past twelve.
(One half hour is 30 minutes.) Write the correct time phrase from
the box below under each clock.

Time Phrases

half past 7	12:30
half past 2	5:30
half past 9	4:30
half past 1	3:30

47

Ways to Make 5

Count the apples in each box. Then write the addition sentences.
Example:

1. 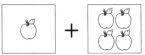 $\underline{1} + \underline{4} = \underline{5}$

2.  $\underline{} + \underline{} = \underline{}$

3. 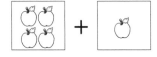 $\underline{} + \underline{} = \underline{}$

4.  $\underline{} + \underline{} = \underline{}$

5.  $\underline{} + \underline{} = \underline{}$

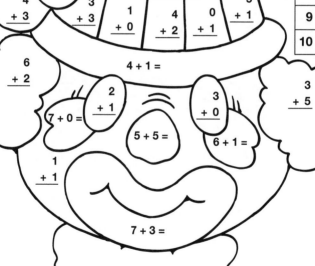

Clowning Around

Add. Color the picture
using the color code.

Color Code

1	pink
2	white
3	black
4	brown
5	purple
6	green
7	blue
8	orange
9	yellow
10	red

$5 + 2 =$

$$\begin{array}{r} 4 \\ + 5 \end{array} \qquad \begin{array}{r} 5 \\ + 0 \end{array}$$

$6 + 3 =$

$$\begin{array}{r} 2 \\ + 3 \end{array} \qquad \begin{array}{r} 7 \\ + 2 \end{array} \qquad \begin{array}{r} 4 \\ + 4 \end{array}$$

$2 + 5 =$

$3 + 2 =$

$$\begin{array}{r} 4 \\ + 3 \end{array} \qquad \begin{array}{r} 3 \\ + 3 \end{array} \qquad \begin{array}{r} 1 \\ + 0 \end{array} \qquad \begin{array}{r} 4 \\ + 2 \end{array} \qquad \begin{array}{r} 0 \\ + 1 \end{array} \qquad \begin{array}{r} 5 \\ + 1 \end{array}$$

$$\begin{array}{r} 6 \\ + 2 \end{array}$$

$4 + 1 =$

$$\begin{array}{r} 3 \\ + 5 \end{array}$$

$7 + 0 =$

$$\begin{array}{r} 2 \\ + 1 \end{array} \qquad \begin{array}{r} 3 \\ + 0 \end{array}$$

$5 + 5 =$

$6 + 1 =$

$$\begin{array}{r} 1 \\ + 1 \end{array}$$

$7 + 3 =$

$3 + 1 =$

Scarecrow Subtraction

Cross out the pictures to solve each problem.

1.

$$6 - 4 = \underline{\hspace{1cm}}$$

2.

$$5 - 3 = \underline{\hspace{1cm}}$$

3.

$$6 - 1 = \underline{\hspace{1cm}}$$

Trucking Along

Subtract. Color the picture using the color code.

Color Code

0	white
1	brown
2	black
3	green
4	purple
5	orange
6	yellow
7	blue
8	red

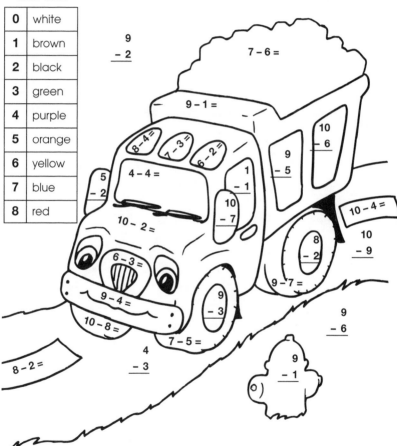

WRITING

A-M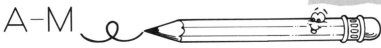

Trace and write.

A   B   C   D

E   F   G   H   I

J   K   L   M

N–Z

Trace and write.

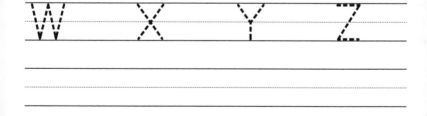

a – m

Trace and write.

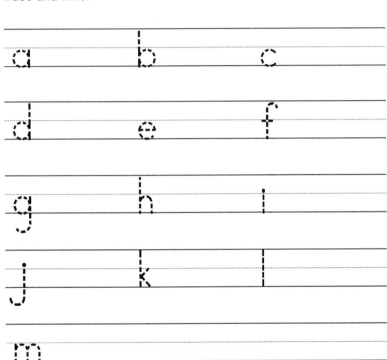

n – z

Trace and write.

n   o   p

q   r   s

t   u   v

w   x   y

z

1–5

Trace and write.

1 1

2 2

3 3

4 4

5 5

6-10

Trace and write.

6   6

7   7

8   8

9   9

10   10

Number Words

Trace and write.

1 one

2 two

3 three

4 four

5 five

60

More Number Words

Trace and write.

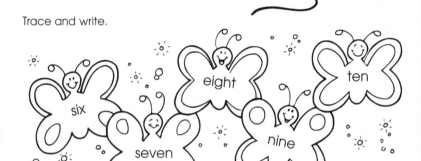

6 six

7 seven

8 eight

9 nine

10 ten

Color Words

Trace and write.

red

yellow

blue

green

orange

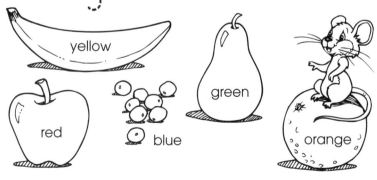

yellow

red

blue

green

orange

More Color Words

Trace and write.

purple

brown

black

white

pink

pink

purple

brown

black

white

Months

Jan. Feb. March April May June

Trace and write.

January

February

March

April

May

June

Months

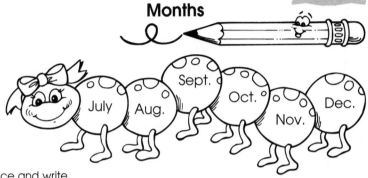

Trace and write.

July

August

September

October

November

December

Days of the Week

Trace and write.

Sunday

Monday

Tuesday

Wednesday

Thursday

Friday

Saturday

GRAMMAR

That's Amazing!

Help the mouse through the maze by coloring each box with a word that begins with a capital letter.

The	For	That	with	know	but
here	on	When	Have	next	we
as	after	good	Make	there	see
Go	Look	Are	Could	is	why
This	who	said	in	come	them
Has	Name	Before	Her	Where	The

Capitalize First Word

Read each sentence. Then fill in the circle next to the word with the capital letter that begins the sentence.

1. **The cat is in the van.**

   ◯ cat

   ◯ The

2. **My dog can run.**

   ◯ My

   ◯ dog

3. **Jan can hop.**

   ◯ Jan

   ◯ hop

4. **I like ham.**

   ◯ ham

   ◯ I

5. **Ants like jam.**

   ◯ jam

   ◯ Ants

In the Rain Forest

Unscramble the words to make a sentence. Write the new sentence. Do not forget to put a period at the end.

1.
A hiding jaguar is

_____

_____

_____

2.
blue Some butterflies are

_____

_____

_____

3.   **water in jump the Frogs**

_____

_____

_____

_____

_____

4.   **snakes trees Green hang from**

_____

_____

_____

_____

_____

High-Flying Sentences

Color each flag that tells a complete thought. Leave the other flags blank.

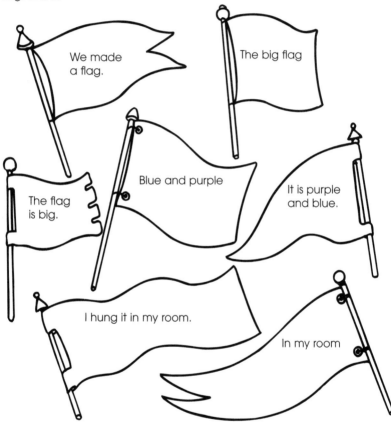

We made a flag.

The big flag

Blue and purple

The flag is big.

It is purple and blue.

I hung it in my room.

In my room

Periods

A telling sentence ends with a period.

Write a period where it belongs in each sentence. Read the sentences to a friend.

1. **Dan is in the cab**

2. **The cat is in the cab**

3. **Mom is in the cab**

4. **We see Dan and Mom**

Read the words. Write each word at the end of the correct sentence.

| van.   red. |

5. **We can go in the** _____

6. **The van is** _____

Periods

Read each group of words. Fill in the circle next to the correct sentence.

1.

Ⓐ **The cat is on the mat.**

Ⓑ **the cat is on the mat**

Ⓒ **the cat on the mat**

2.

Ⓐ **the rat is on the mop**

Ⓑ **the rat is on the mop**

Ⓒ **The rat is on the mop.**

3.

Ⓐ **The rat sees the cat**

Ⓑ **The rat sees the cat.**

Ⓒ **the rat sees the cat**

4.

Ⓐ **The rat can hop.**

Ⓑ **The rat can hop**

Ⓒ **the rat can hop**

5.

Ⓐ **the cat and rat sit**

Ⓑ **The cat and rat sit**

Ⓒ **The cat and rat sit.**

LOGIC

Size It Up

Draw a ◇ around the picture that is **short**.

Draw a ◇ around the picture that is **long**.

Transportation Station

Draw a ▭ around the picture that is **big**.

Draw a ▭ around the picture that is **small**.

Searching for Opposites

An elephant is big. A mouse is little.
Big and little are **opposites**.

Circle the picture that shows the opposite.

happy	sad
up	down
boy	girl
fast	slow

Searching for More Opposites

Circle the picture that shows the **opposite**.

big   little

in   out

hot   cold

full   empty

Different as Can Be

Follow the maze to match the pictures that show the opposite.

A Perfect Match

 and are the **same**.

Connect the cars that are the same.

What Comes Next?

Circle the shape that comes next.

○ □ ○ □ ○	○ □
△ ▯ △ ▯ △	▯ △
⬭ ◇ ○ ⬭ ◇	○ ◇
◇ ▯ △ ◇ ▯	◇ △

Decorate a Headband

Draw the shapes that finish the patterns.

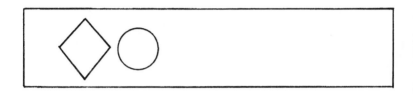

What Comes Next?

Draw the shapes to complete each pattern.

1.

2.

3.

Button Patterns

Finish labeling each pattern.

1.

A   B   A   B   ____   ____

2.

A   A   B   A   ____   ____

3.

A   B   C   A   ____   ____

Everything in Order

The **sequence** is the order in which things happen.

Write 1 under the picture that happens first.
Write 2 under the picture that happens second.

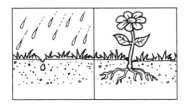

_____   _____

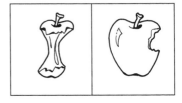

_____   _____

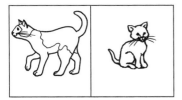

_____   _____

_____   _____

_____   _____

_____   _____

Perfect Order

Write 1 by what happened first.
Write 2 by what happened second.
Write 3 by what happened third.

Side by Side

Draw a line to match the pictures that go together.

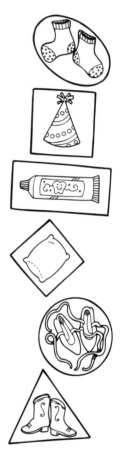

Together Is Better

Color the picture that goes with the first picture in each row.

Out of Place

Put an **X** on the picture that does not belong.

What's Missing?

Look at each set of pictures below. What is missing from the pictures on the right side? Draw what's missing to make both pictures the same.

What's Different?

Look at the top and bottom pictures. Are they exactly the same?
Circle the three things you see in the bottom picture that are not in
the top picture.

You Can Draw a Balloon!

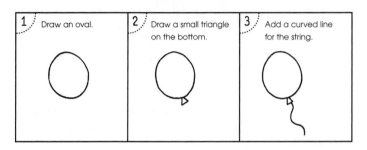

1 Draw an oval.

2 Draw a small triangle on the bottom.

3 Add a curved line for the string.

You Can Draw a Kite!

1 Draw a diamond.	**2** Draw a line from the top to the bottom.	**3** Draw a line from left to right.
4 Draw a curvy line for the string.	**5** Draw 2 small triangles on the left side of the string.	**6** Draw 2 small triangles on the right side of the string.

You Can Draw a Dinosaur!

1 Draw a small circle for the head.	**2** Draw a large oval for the body.	**3** Connect the head and body with two lines.
4 Draw a curved triangle for the tail.	**5** Draw four rectangles for legs.	**6** Add facial features, spots, and toes.

Show What You Know

1. Which one is the same?

2. Which one is different?

3. Which animal name begins with the same sound?

4. Which animal name rhymes?